Maori legends for young New Zealanders

by Katarina Mataira
Drawings by Clare Bowes

bfp Books for Pleasure
A division of Paul Hamlyn Pty. Limited
Sydney, Auckland, London, New York.

Published by Paul Hamlyn Limited,
Levien Building, St Paul Street,
Auckland, New Zealand.

First published 1975
© Copyright Paul Hamlyn Limited 1975
Reprinted 1977

Typeset in New Zealand by Jacobson Typesetters Ltd
Printed by Toppan Printing Co., Singapore
ISBN 0 600 07378 5

Editor: Christine Harris

CONTENTS

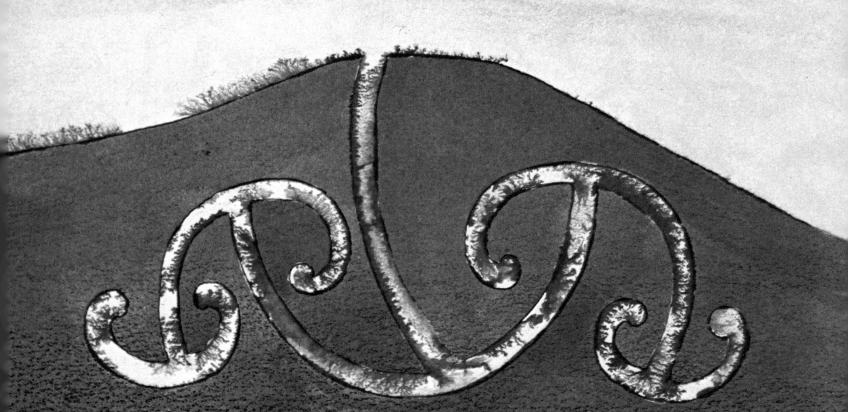

IN THE BEGINNING

In the beginning there was nothing. There was not anything but a great, long, black night. Nothing moved, nothing whispered. The night of no beginning was absolutely still and absolutely silent. Then in the darkness there was a twitch, a shudder, a shake, and a tiny curl began to form. In the midst of the vast, black, empty space the small curl began to grow. It curled, it eddied, it swirled and swelled. It grew bigger and bigger until it became a gigantic wave. Across the space it swept, swishing and swirling, twisting and twirling. It gathered a million particles of stardust until, heaving under its own great weight, it crashed upon the shores of heaven. A million particles of flame were hurled into emptiness.

Light thrust away the empty darkness and, lo, there in the dimness was Rangi the sky, and there in the starlight was Papa the earth.

The sleeping Rangi awoke with a start. He opened his eyes and looked about him. 'What is this?' he cried, 'What beauty, what wonder, what glory is this?' The sleeping earth awoke. 'Wonderful, wonderful, wonderful', she cried as she stretched herself in the dawning light. Rangi twirled his cloak of iridescent blue and looked downward, and Papa raised her face to the light. Each looked at the other and could not look away. Rangi reached downward and wrapped his cloak about the earth. Papa reached her arms upwards to embrace the sky, and together they loved and became man and wife.

THE SONS OF RANGI AND PAPA

For many years Rangi and Papa floated in space. For many years they clung to each other; they dared not let go lest they became separated again. Many sons were born to them. There was Tanemahutu, tall and very clever. There was Tawhirimatea with the mighty voice. There was Tangaroa as wild as the sea, and Tu-matauenga the warrior. There was gentle Rongo who loved the earth and Haumia gentler still, and there was Ruaumoko, the playful, volcanic Ruaumoko.

The brothers were all very strong young men, but they had never walked on two legs. The earth and sky were so close together that it was quite impossible for them to stand up. They were trapped between their parents. Haumia and Rongo did not mind too much. They loved the warm dimness of the earth. So did Ruaumoko, but Tane and Tu and Tangaroa were soon protesting very loudly.

'I want to feel my strength. I want to wave my arms and stamp my feet,' cried Tu. 'I want to swing my axe and throw my spear. I need space, space!'

Tane was also unhappy. 'Our world is just too stifling,' he said, 'and much too cramped. We need space to move around in and we must have more light and more air.'

Tangaroa agreed most emphatically. 'Let us do something, brothers', he said. 'This cannot go on. We must do something.'

'There is only one thing to do,' said Tu.

'What is that?' asked the brothers.

'We shall have to kill our father and mother,' said Tu. There was a gasp of astonishment.

'No, no, no, no,' cried the brothers in anguish, 'that will never do. Never, never, never!' And they argued among themselves.

Above the noise the thunderous voice of Tawhirimatea rolled forth. 'If you as much as ruffle the cloak of my father or the hair of my mother,' he said, 'I shall wage war against you forever.'

The other brothers quivered with fright, but Tu was not at all intimidated. 'War against me, indeed! I am the fighter. I am the warrior. How dare you challenge me?'

'Hush,' remonstrated Tane. 'Let us not argue. Perhaps we can do something else.'

'What can we do?' questioned Tangaroa.

'Well, why don't we separate our parents?' suggested Tane.

'Oh,' said the gentle Rongo, 'that would be so cruel. Please leave them alone. Please let us remain as we are.'

'You may be happy as you are,' growled Tu, 'but I'm not. You may enjoy grovelling on the ground, but I don't. I still say we should kill our parents, for how else can we separate them?'

Tawhirimatea's anger showed plainly in the flash of his eyes. 'I have warned you,' he said and departed.

Haumia and Rongo also left, sad that their brothers should contemplate such treachery. Only Tu and Tangaroa and Tane remained.

'Well, my clever brothers,' said Tu, 'what brilliant idea have you got? It had better be good or I shall do what I believe needs to be done."

'If we could just push them apart,' Tane suggested.

'How will you do that?' questioned Tu.

'I shan't, brother', said Tane, 'but I am sure one of you could. You and Tangaroa are the strongest by far.'

'Let me try,' said Tangaroa eagerly.

'No,' said Tu, 'only I can do it. Stand aside and give me room.'

Tane and Tangaroa sat by while Tu crouched, braced his arms and shoulders against his father and then with a mighty thrust of his legs heaved upward. All he managed to do was to snuff out his own breath.

Tangaroa giggled. 'Ha, ha, ha, ha, where is your power, brother? Where is your strength? Why don't you try again?'

Again and again Tu attempted to push his father away from his mother, but to no avail.

'That's it,' he declared in frustration. 'I shall have to kill them.'

'No, wait!' said Tane. 'Let me try.'

'You!' bellowed Tu, 'if I can't do it how can you?'

'Just let me try,' said Tane.

He lay on his back, then, folding his knees against his chest, he placed his feet against his father's belly. He pushed a little and felt his father move. He pushed a little harder and immediately his father's voice rang out.

'What are you doing to me? Stop it at once. Stop it, I say!'

Tane pushed a little harder still. His father was now worried.

'What are you doing down there? I am beginning to slip away. Stop it, stop it, stop it, I say!'

Tane did not hesitate. With a powerful thrust of his legs he levered upward, and Papa hurtled away from Rangi. It all happened so quickly that for a moment there was a stunned silence. Then a great roar emanated from Tawhirimatea, and without warning he loosed lightning and thunder and violent storms upon his brothers.

Haumia and Rongo buried themselves in the ground. Tangaroa and Tane fled for the safety of a deep cave. Only Tu stood his ground.

'You will never defeat me,' he cried. 'Never.'

Indeed, after many days and nights of battle it was

Tawhirimatea who grew tired first. He decided that the battle could continue another time, and he went off into space to join his father. Behind him remained a still defiant Tu, a scattering of great oceans, and a desolate earth.

Poor Rangi and Papa, from that day to this they have yearned for each other. Sometimes we can feel their sorrow in the rise of the early morning mist or the touch of softly falling rain.

CHILDREN OF THE GODS

When the last flash of Tawhirimatea's anger had faded away, Tumatauenga stood astride the mountain. Triumphantly he thumped his chest and shouted across the empty valleys of Mother Earth, 'I am Tumatauenga the Mighty, and I shall rule the earth!'

From mountain to mountain the voice echoed and re-echoed until finally hushed in the stillness. Then Tu suddenly realised he was all alone. Where were his brothers? He looked everywhere but could not see them.

'So!' he shouted again. 'So, my cowardly brothers, you hide from me, do you? And you may well hide, for I shall hunt you and strike you down. Never shall I forgive you for abandoning me.'

Hearing his terrible voice, Haumia and Rongo shivered and burrowed deeper into the rich brown earth. Tangaroa and Tane, however, heeded him not at all, for they were much too busy.

Tane had been racing across the land, revelling in the space and the sunlight. A million sleeping spirits crowded the earth, and when Tane touched each of them they brought forth living things — birds and bees, flowers and trees, butterflies of every colour — and to these, his children, Tane spoke softly, 'Come, my children,' he said. 'Cluster close to the body of my mother, spread your beauty across her nakedness and keep her warm.'

To the birds and singing insects he said, 'And you, my lovelies, tilt your throats and beat your wings. Let your music rise to soothe my mother's unhappiness.'

Drunk with these joys of creation, Tane found a lump of clay. He shook it an breathed onto it. Behold, a woman came into being. Tane called her Hine-ahu-one and married her, and a daughter as beautiful as the dawn was born to them.

Meanwhile, beneath the sea and safe from the threats of Tu, Tangaroa strode about. He filled the water with fishes — long ones, short ones, fat ones, flat ones, fish large and small, some with tails, some with fins, some with scales, and some with shells. The rivers, lakes, and seas teemed with the silvery children of Tangaroa.

And in the warm earth, dampened by the tears of Rangi, Haumia and Rongo swelled and gave forth their offspring — the trees, punga, and the succulent ferns.

But high up in the heavens, next to the Sky Father, Tawhirimatea grumbled and growled. He was still smarting at the memory of the defiant Tu.

'I will fix him,' he muttered. 'I'll fix that cheeky Tu. But I must have children to aid me in my battle against him.'

So he brought forth the hurricane, the cyclone, and the tempest, but Tu continued to stride about the earth without a care.

'Let him do what he will,' Tu was unconcerned. Right now, all he wished was to find his brothers so that he might box their ears. He did not find Tane nor Tangaroa, nor Haumia nor Rongo, but he discovered their children springing from the earth.

Wrapping the curling leaves of the fern about his wrists, Tu wrenched and tugged. The fern root resisted and clung stubbornly to the soil, but Tu would not give in. With a sharpened stick he dug the soil away from around the roots until they had to yield. And now he would capture those pretty birds and darting fishes.

'How will I catch them,?' he asked himself. He laughed jubilantly when in answer he spied some slender young saplings in Tane's forest.

With sharpened points, the saplings made wicked spears. Alas, many birds and fishes fell prey to the swift and straight aim of Tu. The fern root, the fat pigeon, and the fishes of the sea, all were killed and eaten by the voracious Tu as he revelled in his victories.

But Tu soon came to realise that alone he could not capture all the children of his brothers. There were myriads of them, and they were increasing rapidly. There was only one answer. He must have his own children to harrass Tane and tease Tangaroa, to pinch and plunder Haumia and Rongo. But how was he to create children? He had not the creative power of his brothers.

As he thought on this, Tu was wandering through the forests of Tane, and quite by chance he came across the beautiful Hine-ahu-one. Hine was looking very unhappy, so Tu approached her.

'Why are you sad, Hine?' he asked.

Hine did not reply, so Tu again said, 'Why are you sad, Hine?'

'Why do you ask?' was Hine's reply. 'You cannot help me.'

'But perhaps I can, said Tu. 'Tell me what ails you.'

'My husband has abandoned me,' Hine said hesitantly, brushing away a tear. 'He spends all of his time pursuing the beautiful dawn maid. I am alone and forgotten.'

'Ha,' said Tu, 'then he does not deserve you. Why waste your time fretting? Come away with me and forget him.'

Hine hesitated.

'Hine,' Tu insisted, 'come with me.'

Hine hesitated no longer. She went with Tu and became his wife, and through her the child of Tu was born. That child was man.

The children of the gods increased and filled the earth, but they were the children of Tu who reigned supreme. Like Tu they were bold, like Tu they learnt to fish and hunt, and not the winds of Tawhiri nor the great seas of Tangaroa could intimidate them. Across land and sea they spread until they had encompassed the earth.

MAKO AND TUATARA

Man ruled the earth, but whenever they could the children of Tangaroa fought back. Of all the children of Tangaroa, Mako the shark and Tuatara the giant lizard were the most feared, for they had great mouths and sawlike teeth. Few men could win a battle against these warriors of Tangaroa.

One day Mako and Tuatara were cruising lazily backwards and forwards in a beautiful bay. Both had been sent by Tangaroa to guard the bay and to keep a lookout for men. Any man who stepped into the water they were to attack. Both were feeling hungry, for they had not eaten in a long time.

'I'm so hungry,' said Mako, 'I hope a large fishing party arrives shortly. I could eat a hundred men.'

Tuatara fastened his eyes on the shore and they glowed with pleasure as he said, 'Ssh! Lie still. I see a fishing party.'

Mako could not see the fishing party for he had to stay under the water. His tell-tale fin had often scared men away and caused him to miss a tasty meal.

'How many?' he asked.

'Perhaps fifty,' answered Tuatara.

'That will do for a small meal,' said Mako.

'But only four of them are climbing aboard the canoe,' observed Tuatara.

'Bother!' Mako exclaimed.

They drifted out to sea and waited in deeper water.

'I knew it,' came Tuatara's voice suddenly. 'They are heading for the reef where many of our little brothers live.'

The dipping paddles of the canoe soon sent a stream of bubbles towards Mako and Tuatara. Mako was worried.

'How can we attack them?' he asked. 'As long as they stay in the canoe they are safe.'

'Then I shall tip them out of the canoe,' decided Tuatara.

And straight away he sped towards the canoe. One of the men saw him.

'It's the taniwha!' he screamed.

The rowers swung round and raised their paddles. Tuatara glimpsed the fear in their eyes as he approached, and when the paddles began lashing at him he dived under the canoe. The paddles could not touch him there. He knew that Mako must be close by. All he had to do was to capsize the canoe. So he curled his tail under the canoe and thrust it upwards. The small craft flew into the air and came down with a mightly splash, turning all the men into the water. With flashing tail and gnashing jaws Mako closed in.

In a matter of minutes the men had disappeared and Mako was cruising lazily back into the shallows to bask in the sun. Tuatara was furious.

'You've eaten them all!' he cried. 'You left none for me, and it was I who did the hard work.'

'I'm sorry,' said Mako, 'but they were really so few and I did not think you would be offended.'

'But why? There were more men on the beach. Look.'

Tuatara looked. Indeed, all the people of the village were on the beach. They had seen what had happened and had come down to investigate. None, however, had dared to come near the water.

'They are too afraid to come into the water now,' said Tuatara glumly.

'Then why don't you go to them?' suggested Mako. 'You have legs and feet. You can walk. Think how pleased Tangaroa would be if you attacked the village.'

'That is true,' agreed Tuatara. 'Why did I not think of that before?'

And he swam towards the village folk. When he raised himself out of the water and lumbered out on his clumsy feet, the people recoiled in horror. With his flicking tongue, bulging eyes, and bristling dorsel spine, Tuatara was an awesome sight.

Some of the men threw stones and sticks, but these bounced harmlessly off Tuatara's scaly skin. The people turned and fled. Men and women gathered up little children as they raced up the beach, all the while screaming, 'Taniwha! Taniwha! Run!'

Tuatara lumbered up the village, but when he arrived not a single person remained. He walked right through the village, crunching the flimsy houses to a pile of broken sticks under his huge feet. When he had flattened every house he returned to the beach. Mako was impressed.

'Tuatara, you shall be famous,' he said. 'Of all the children of Tangaroa, you alone have won the first great victory against the children of Tu.'

Tuatara was pleased with this praise.

'Perhaps I should stay here,' he said. 'Did you see how many men there were? Perhaps they will come back. I shall hide and wait for them.'

Yet Mako was not so enthusiastic.

'I think you will be safer in the sea,' he ventured. 'You move very slowly on land.'

'That does not matter,' said Tuatara. 'Did you not see how their weapons bounced off my back? Besides, it is very pleasant here. The sun is warm, and the grass underfoot is so comfortable. Yes, I think I shall stay.'

Mako was growing anxious now.

'Please, Tuatara, come back. You will be safer.'

'No, my mind is made up,' Tuatara was firm.

'Alas, Tuatara,' said Mako sadly, 'if you stay, men will hunt you down and kill you.'

'I will stay,' said Tuatara.

'Goodbye, then,' bade Mako, and he swam away.

'Remember me,' called Tuatara, 'and beware the hooks of men lest they drag you out of the sea to roast you in their ovens.'

Mako did not hear. He was already far out to sea, wondering how long it would be before Tuatara disappeared from the face of the earth.

MAUI SNARES THE SUN

During this olden time the days were very short and the nights very long. The sun travelled across the sky so quickly that the people did not have enough time to complete their tasks during daylight hours. The men could not dig their gardens or fish or hunt. The women had very little time to weave their mats and the children never had enough time to play. Very soon the people began to grumble.

'We cannot dig our gardens,' growled the men, 'or fish or hunt.'

'We cannot weave out mats,' growled the women.

'We cannot play,' grizzled the children.

'If only the days were longer,' everyone grumbled, but nobody could do anything about it. The sun continued to speed across the sky. The people continued to complain and the children continued to grizzle.

'Something should be done,' everyone shouted, but nobody could do anything.

There was in the village a very clever young man called Maui. He listened to the women complaining, heard the children grizzling, and hearkened to the voices of the men. They were shouting, 'We must do something,' but Maui just shrugged his shoulders. 'If the days were longer,' he thought, 'we would all have to work longer.' Maui was rather lazy and saw no reason to work any more than was necessary.

One day he said to his wife, 'Woman, I am very hungry. Light the fire and cook me some food.'

His wife lit the fire at once and placed her cooking stones upon it. But even before the stones were hot the sun went down. The cooking had to be done in the dark and when it was time to eat Maui could not see what he was eating . This annoyed him very much.

'I shall have to make the sun go slower,' he said, and he called his four brothers. The brothers came quickly for they were a little in awe of Maui.

'He knows much magic,' they said, 'and he has a magic weapon.'

'I think,' said Maui, 'that we shall have to slow down the Sun. We need longer days. We need more daylight. We should not have to grope around in the dark as we do.'

'But what can we do?' asked the brothers. 'What can we do against the powerful Sun.'

Maui was annoyed.

'You disappoint me, brothers,' he said. 'You know that I have many magic powers. You know that I have a magic weapon. How can you doubt me?'

The brothers nodded quietly.

'It is true,' they agreed.'We know these things. Perhaps you are right. Tell us what we must do.'

'First you must gather some flax,' said Maui, 'and then you must make an enormous noose.'

The brothers did as they were told. It was the largest and strongest noose anyone had ever seen.

'Now we must find the pit from which the sun emerges,' said Maui.

'Where is that?' asked the brothers.

'On the other side of the earth,' answered Maui, 'away towards the east.'

'But that is such a long way away,' moaned the brothers.

'Indeed it is,' said Maui, 'so we will start off tonight as soon as the Sun sets.'

They travelled all night and, when the glow in the sky told them that the Sun was rising, they hid themselves.

'The Sun must not see us,' said Maui.

So from sunrise to sunset they rested, and during the night they travelled. After many days and nights they came at last to the other side of the earth. The brothers were very tired and wanted to sleep but Maui would not let them.

'Look over there,' he commanded, pointing to an enormous hole in the ground. 'That is the pit from which the Sun emerges. Look at the scorched ground. If you sleep now, the Sun will surely burn you to a cinder when he emerges.'

'We won't sleep. We won't sleep,' the brothers said quickly. 'Tell us what we should do now.'

'We must first build a high wall of clay around the pit. Then each of you must build yourselves a shelter behind the wall.'

The brothers set to work at once. They worked furiously, and when the wall and shelters were ready the noose was fixed across the pit.

'Hurry,' yelled Maui. 'I see a glimmer in the pit.'

The brothers each grabbed a corner of the noose and ran nervously towards their shelters.

'Hurry,' yelled Maui again. 'I see a glow in the pit.'

'We are ready,' called the anxious brothers.

'Then listen carefully,' Maui ordered. 'Do not pull the noose ropes until I say so. When I call, then, and only then, will you pull. But you must all pull at the same time, and you must hold tight no matter what happens.'

The glow in the pit was getting brighter. Maui crouched behind the clay wall, and, holding his magic weapon, he chanted a magic spell:

> Make the noose strong, make the noose tight,
> Not fire nor heat shall render it.
> Give my weapon strength, give my weapon might,
> Not fire nor heat shall render it.
> Give me strength give me might,
> Not fire nor heat shall render me.

The glow in the pit had deepened to a fiery red. Tongues of flame began to lick out of the pit. The heat cracked the clay wall and singed the grass on the surrounding hills. The flaming head of the Sun appeared, then his shoulders. He rose upwards straight into the noose.

Maui yelled to his brothers, 'Pull on the ropes.'

The noose tightened, and the Sun was trapped.

'Who dares to play tricks on the Sun?' shouted the angry Sun as he struggled to free himself. He blew a great tongue of flame at the ropes but the ropes would not burn.

'What silly game is this?' he screamed, and he blew another flame at the ropes. Still the ropes would not burn.

Then Maui sprang out from behind the wall and lashed at the Sun with his magic weapon. The Sun screamed with pain, but Maui continued to beat him.

'Stop!' cried the Sun, 'Why do you treat me like this?'

Maui kept on swinging blows at the Sun's head, taking no notices of his screams.

'What are you doing, Man, what are you doing? Why do you wish to kill me?'

Still Maui took no notice. He swung his magic weapon until he was exhausted. Only then did he bid his brothers to loosen the rope.

Then the Sun rose slowly and painfully into the sky to go on his way, now so lame that he could only limp very, very slowly.

So it was that the days became longer. So it was that the men were able to dig their gardens and fish and hunt. So it was that the women were able to do their weaving, and the children play for hours and hours. And Maui was able at last to enjoy his food because he could see what he was eating.

THE PET WHALE

On the beautiful island of Motutapu there lived a chief called Tinirau and his son Tuhuruhuru. One day Tuhuruhuru came to his father looking very unhappy.

'Father,' he said, 'I must speak with you.'

'What troubles you, my son?' asked Tinirau.

Tuhuruhuru hesitated for a moment, then blurted out, 'My mother, I want to know about my mother. I had thought her to be dead, but my playmates taunt me about her. They say that she is not dead, that she left me because she does not love me. Is it true, Father?'

Tinirau thought awhile before replying.

'It is true, son, that she left you. But it is not true that she did so because she did not love you.'

'Then why did she leave?' questioned Tuhuruhuru.

Tinirau hesitated again.

'Will you promise not to hate me if I tell you?' he asked. 'For I have been very unkind in the past.'

'I cannot hate you,' said Tu. 'You are my father.'

'Hush, then,' answered Tinirau, 'and I will tell you.'

Tuhuruhuru settled himself at his father's feet, and Tinirau said, 'Your mother came here a long time ago. We found her on the beach near to dying, for she had floated in from the sea. She recovered, however, and some time later she became my wife.'

'For a long time we were very happy, then we quarrelled, and I was so angry that I sent her from my house. For many months she lived alone, and I made no attempt to see her until I learned that you had been born. I tried then to see her but she would not receive me.

'When her brother arrived a little later to take her home I could not stop her from going with him. However she did agree to leave you with me.'

Tuhuruhuru wanted to cry, but a chief's son must never do that, so he fought back the tears and said, 'Father, I must go to her.'

Tinirau nodded his head.

'And if I can,' added Tuhuruhuru, 'I shall bring her back again.'

So Tuhuruhuru took a canoe and some provisions and paddled away to the island home of his mother. Tinirau could not be sure that Tuhuruhuru would ever return, for the great distances between the islands were frought with danger. He had lost his wife a long time ago. Perhaps now his son also would be lost to him.

One day as he sat before his house trying not to think too much about the dangers his son would encounter, a boy came running to him.

'Come quickly!' he cried. 'There is a whale on the beach. It's stranded on the sand!'

Tinirau went at once. The village people had all gathered on the beach and were flushed with excitement. The men already had their weapons drawn and were anxious to kill the animal.

'We shall feast well tonight,' they said to their chief happily.

But Tinirau looked at the whale and thought, 'What a beautiful animal! It is far too beautiful to kill. Besides, if I am kind to a child of Tangaroa perhaps he will protect my son in return.'

So deciding, he said to the people, 'No, we will not feast well tonight. Put down your weapons. This animal is far too beautiful to kill. Let us save him.' There was a deadly silence. The people were disappointed, and some of the men protested.

'It will die anyway,' they said. 'How we can save it?'

Then, waving his arm at every man, woman, and child, Tinirau said, 'Go, all of you. Fetch gourds and bring them here.' The people went quickly, and when they returned their chief spoke again.

'Now fill the gourds with seawater and bathe the animal. We will have to keep him wet and cool until the tide turns and he can swim away again.'

The people obeyed. For many hours they carried water from the sea and poured it over the whale while Tinirau stroked and patted him. From time to time he checked to see that the whale's breathing hole was free from sand. Sometimes he whistled a soothing melody. The whale had ceased to thrash about and lay quietly, enjoying the administrations of Tinirau and his people.

The people, too, were now much happier. They could see that the whale would not die, and they began to sing as they carried their gourds of water back and forth from the sea. At last the tide turned, and before long the water was deep enough for the whale to move. When he flipped his tail and moved majestically away the people cheered happily. They did not feast well that evening but they talked long into the night about how kind and clever was their chief.

For the first time since his son had left, Tinirau slept soundly. Not until the first flickers of early morning did he dream, and then it was a pleasant dream. He dreamt that his wife and son were riding home upon the back of the whale.

Later on that morning Tinirau was wakened by excited voices, and as he rose from his bed he noticed that the people were all rushing down to the beach.

'Look!' they cried, 'The whale! It is back!'

Tinirau dressed quickly and joined the people on the beach. There in the bay, swimming sedately up and down, was the whale. Tinirau called for a canoe, and he and some of the men paddled out into the bay. When they were still some distance from the whale Tinirau bade the men stop paddling. Then he stood up and whistled. The whale had been swimming away from them, but when the whistle wafted across the bay he turned and came up alongside the canoe and lay there. The men cheered as Tinirau reached out to stroke the whale, laughing and chatting to it as though he were an old friend.

'You will be as a son to me,' said Tinirau, 'and I will call you Tutunui.'

Then to everyone's amazement Tinirau climbed over the gunwale of the canoe and onto the whale's back. There was a moment of breathless silence. What would the whale do? Would he fight? Would he die? Would he capsize the canoe? But the whale did none of these things. Slowly he moved away from the canoe, and with great thrusts of his tail he headed out to the open sea.

There was a moment of panic among the astonished people. One of the paddlers in the canoe immediately commanded the others to take up their paddles.

'Quickly,' he said, 'put all your strength into your paddling. We must keep up with the whale lest he take a dive and drown Tinirau.'

Muscles bulged on the sweaty backs of the paddlers as they dipped in time. Never had they paddled so rapidly before. Yet still they could not build up enough speed to catch up with the whale. Tinirau was soon just a speck on the horizon, and the paddlers could only return home.

The people of Motutapu waited on the shore all morning, hoping that a miracle might happen and their chief return. In the afternoon all the men launched their canoes to search for their chief, but they returned in the evening tired and convinced that their chief had gone forever. They were all about to return to their homes when someone cried, 'Look! There upon the horizon I see something.'

People strained their eyes to see. Yes, indeed, there was something. Dared they hope it was Tinirau? Some of the people climbed to the clifftops where they might get a better view. It was growing dark and it was very difficult to see clearly, but the speck on the horizon did appear to be getting larger. Then the whale came into sight, and still sitting astride his back was Tinirau. A great shout of applause echoed along the beach as the people dragged every canoe down to the water and paddled out to meet their chief.

That evening everyone gathered in the meeting house to listen to the story of Tinirau's adventure. Long into the night they sat enthralled as Tinirau told of the islands he had visited and of the places in the ocean where fish teemed in their thousands.

From that day on, whenever a fishing expedition or a visit to another island was planned, Tinirau travelled upon the back of the whale. His fame travelled far and wide, and men envied his good fortune. When several months later his wife and son returned, Tinirau's happiness was complete.

THE TREACHEROUS KAE

An aura of excitement settled upon the island of Motutapu as the people prepared for a great celebration. The men had gone fishing and hunting. Some of the women and children were gathering shellfish down in the rock pools, and the others had gone to the forest to collect fruits and berries. Huge holes had been dug in the ground to receive the large quantities of food.

Tinirau had decided that special ceremonies should accompany this celebration which was in honour of his son. A priest was necessary, so a canoe had been sent to a neighbouring island to fetch the famous priest whose name was Kae.

Kae was very pleased to come to Motutapu. When he arrived all the preparations had been made, and all the people were assembled. The ceremonies were duly performed. Then it was time for the magnificent feast, and everything was laid out before Kae.

Tinirau was so pleased with the manner in which the ceremonies had been conducted that he decided he would do something very special for Kae. He walked to the seashore and whistled long and low. Everyone was stilled. Kae wondered what Tinirau was doing. Then a speck appeared on the horizon. It grew larger and larger. Then through the waves ploughed Tutunui the whale, and he came straight to Tinirau. The chief patted and stroked him, then took a slice of meat from his side. Tutunui did not mind this at all. The meat was cooked and given to the priest. Kae had never before eaten whale meat, and he found it delicious. Silently he wished the whale belonged to him.

After the feast there was dancing and merriment long into the night. Then it was time for Kae to return home. A canoe was made ready but Kae would not climb aboard. Another canoe was made ready but Kae still refused to board it. Tinirau was upset, for he did not wish to displease the priest.

'Please tell me what displeases you,' he said to Kae.

'I'm not displeased,' said Kae. 'You have treated me well. But I would very much like to ride home on your magnificent whale.'

'But, of course,' said Tinirau. He walked again to the seashore and whistled. Straight away Tutunui came ploughing through the waves.

Tinirau helped Kae onto the animal's back and said to him, 'When the whale reaches your island he will stop and shake himself. That is when you must get off.' Kae nodded with a rueful smile.

'Go,' said Tinirau to the whale. 'Take the priest to his home.'

Tutunui flicked his tail and swam away. It was not long before he reached Kae's island and stopped and shook himself, but Kae dug his heels into Tutunui's sides and urged him on. Tutunui obeyed. A little nearer the shore he stopped again and shook himself, but Kae urged him still farther. But by now Tutunui had gone too far and was caught in the sand. The tide was ebbing. He could not move. His air holes became clogged with sand so that he could not breathe, and before long poor Tutunui was dead. The treacherous Kae laughed with glee. He sent his people at once to prepare the cooking fires, for they would feast on Tinirau's whale.

Meanwhile Tinirau was walking up and down the beach on Motutapu, waiting for Tutunui to come back. He had called many times but nothing except the gentle breeze ruffled the smooth waters. Tinirau wondered why the whale had not returned. 'Perhaps he is ill,' he thought, 'or perhaps he has been trapped.' Then a curious smell wafted in with the breeze. Tinirau sniffed and sniffed again. At once he flew into a rage.

'So!' he bellowed, 'So the treacherous Kae has killed my whale! He is feasting on it! What treachery!'

Back in his village Tinirau gathered his men around him.

'This evil deed shall be revenged,' he cried. 'Let us decide how we shall repay the murderous Kae.'

But nobody could think of a suitable plan. At last Tinirau's sister came forward and said, 'Let us, the women, fetch Kae and bring him here.'

She described her plan, and the men agreed that it was a good one. A canoe was prepared and filled with gifts, and in it the group of women set off from the island. As they bent over the paddles calls of good luck floated to them over the calm sea.

Within a short space of time the canoe beached upon foreign sands, and Kae's people came to greet those alighting. The gifts were offered, as was the custom, and news was exchanged with old acquaintances. The evening that followed was marked by feasting, dancing, and singing in which all took part. Nobody had cause for suspicion. Only the guilty Kae felt uneasy at the visit of the women of Motutapu.

It was now very late and people began to droop. One by one they rolled over to sleep — everyone, that is, except Kae and Tinirau's sister. She pretended to sleep but kept a watchful eye on the priest. The cunning Kae was watchful too. The group of women looked harmless, but he was not going to take any risks, so long into the night he stayed awake. He was feeling very drowsy, however, so he decided to sleep while pretending to be still awake. He placed a piece of shiny paua shell over each eye.

In the dark the shell glistened like wide, open eyes. Nobody would have guessed that the priest was asleep, nobody except Tinirau's clever sister. When the whole house was drugged with sleep she wakened her friends, and together they carried the sleeping Kae to their canoe, taking care not to waken him. Not a sound was made.

Swiftly the women paddled home. The sleeping Kae was carried up their beach and into the sleeping house. He was placed, still asleep, by the front centre post where he had lain in his own house.

When the rays of the rising sun peeped through the window next morning, Kae woke up. He had dreamt all night about another whalemeat feast, and, remembering that there was still some meat remaining, he sat up eagerly and called to his slaves, 'Bring me water and more whale meat.' But nobody heeded his call.

'Where are you, you lazy slaves?' he shouted again.

Still nobody answered. A dark shadow moved towards him. It was Tinirau, and Kae knew him at once.

'And what brings Tinirau to my house?' he demanded angrily.

'Your house?' Tinirau said. 'Look about you, treacherous one.'

Kae stared about him but perceived no familiar object. Beyond a sea of angry faces he saw that of Tinirau's sister, and he realised he had been outwitted. He bounded to his feet and made a rush for the door, but his way was barred by a revengeful people. There was no escape for the treacherous Kae.

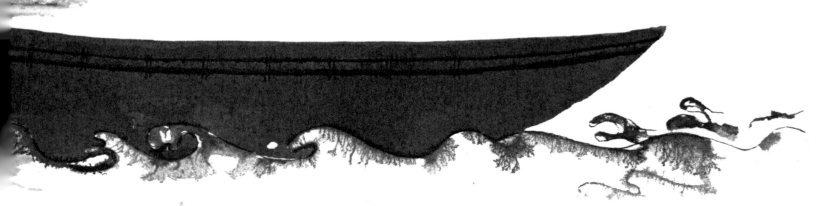

THE GIANT POUAKAI BIRD

A long time ago there lived two brothers called Oriparoa and Manini. One day they went fishing with their friends and followers. They paddled their canoes to a huge rock where there were hundreds of fish, but they anchored their canoes just above that spot where a horrible monster dwelt. When the men threw out their lines the monster rose from the bottom of the sea in a terrible rage. So terrible was his anger that he caused a violent storm to whip up the waves and lash the canoes. All but the canoe of the brothers was overturned.

The canoe of the brothers stayed afloat, but it was carried far out to sea by a mighty wind. For two days and two nights the canoe was at the mercy of the wind. And when the wind dropped the brothers had no idea where they were. Tired, weak, and near to starving they wondered what they should do. Their crew mates were almost dead, and they had neither food nor water.

'There is little hope,' said Manini, 'we are hopelessly lost!' But they did not lose heart and kept a sharp lookout for signs of land. Although they desperately needed to sleep they dared not close their eyes. Instead they trained their eyes upon the horizon and strained their ears to catch every sound above the swishing of the sea.

Then they heard it — a faint far away sound! Yes, there it was again, clearer this time. It was the cry of the oystercatcher.

'There must be land nearby!' exclaimed Manini with relief. Oriparoa nodded happily. Before long the canoe was gliding over patches of seaweed, and the brothers began to pole the canoe. Presently they heard again the call of the oystercatcher and the gull's reply. The brothers poled faster in their excitement. Sure enough, there ahead were the unmistakable lines of a sharp headland.

When the bottom of the canoe scraped sand the brothers climbed overboard and pushed their vessel onto the beach. Immediately Oriparoa drew out his fire-making sticks and rubbed them vigorously together over a pile of dry seaweed. Red sparks

flew from the sticks and ignited the seaweed. Dry twigs were piled onto the flame, and soon a bright fire was crackling.

The rocks on the beach were thick with mussels, and the brothers gathered some of these and placed them on the fire to cook. When the shells began to gape open they were taken from the fire and prised open. Saliva dripped from the brother's mouths, so sweet and succulent the mussels looked. But first they must attend their crew mates.

The helpless men were dragged from the canoe to the fireside, and the brothers fed them till one by one they began to recover. Oriparoa then began to make some bird snares, and he went off into the scrub to lay them. He found a grove of trees teeming with tui and before long he had trapped many of them. Roasted golden brown and dripping in their own tasty juices, the birds were thoroughly enjoyed by all. Everyone had fully recovered, and while they rested one of the men asked Oriparoa whether he had seen any people.

'No,' said Oriparoa, 'not a single person. Yet someone must have lived here. Everywhere there are signs of men.'

The next day Oriparoa and Manini explored farther. Along the beach they went, passing the first and then the second headland until they came to a cave.

'I wonder if there is anything in there,' said Manini.

'Let's take a look,' said Oriparoa.

At the mouth of the cave they peered in. There sat a very old woman all by herself, eating what appeared to be whale meat. Furthermore, she seemed to be eating it raw. She stared in surprise when she saw the brothers and said, 'Where do you come from, the east or the west?'

'Then we are kin,' stated the old woman and invited them to share her meal. The brothers accepted the raw meat she offered but could not eat it. Instead Oriparoa drew out his fire-making sticks again and placed one of them beneath the woman's feet. At once he began to rub the sticks, but before the smoke had even started to curl the old woman felt the growing heat under her feet and threw herself on the ground in terror.

'Fire! Fire!' she screamed, 'The land is on fire!'

Oriparoa withdrew and hastened to his bird traps. More tuis

had been snared and he brought them back to the cave and cooked them. The old woman was now in a dead faint so Oriparoa forced down her throat some of the juices from the cooked birds. she recovered and accepted the birds which Oriparoa offered her. She ate them slowly, picking at the tender flesh and licking the sweet juices from her fingers. Then she smiled.

'Ah!' she said, 'this is delicious food indeed!'

'Do you not cook your food?' asked the brothers.

'No,' replied the woman, 'we eat it raw. We have never learned to cook.'

Later the brothers asked, 'Where are the rest of your people?'

'They have all been eaten,' replied the woman.

'Eaten!' exclaimed the brothers, 'By what?'

'By what indeed!' said the woman, 'By the Pouakai!'

'What on earth is that?' asked the brothers.

'It is a bird,' replied the woman, 'a giant bird. The span of one of its wings is three metres! It will eat you too if it sees you. I have survived only because the cave entrance is small. The bird cannot get in. But it comes often and thrusts its beak or its wings into the cave to try to catch me. I dare not go outside.'

'And where does this monster live?' asked the brothers.

'If you walk along the beach to the tenth headland,' said the woman, 'you will find it.'

Oriparoa went off to the canoe to fetch his crew mates, and on their return they all sat down to discuss the matter.

'What shall we do?' they asked the woman.

'I don't know,' she replied.

'Then tell us how the creature catches it's prey!'

'When it spies a man, it sweeps down from the sky, scoops him up with its wing, and throws him into its mouth.'

The men shivered and looked anxiously at the cave entrance. Oriparoa thought about the problem, however, and then said, 'I think I know what we can do.'

'What? Tell us what!' exclaimed the men.

'Let us build a huge house,' said Oriparoa, 'a special sort of house. The walls shall be formed by living trees. We shall leave their roots in the ground but lop off their tops. And only the centre posts of the house shall be loosely fixed.'

Nobody quite understood what the house was supposed to achieve, but all worked quickly until it was finished. They assembled again at the cave.

'What do we do now? they asked.' We must capture the Pouakai! We must capture it and kill it!'

Oriparoa then said, 'We must somehow lure the bird to the house. Will you tell us how we can do this, old woman?'

The old woman looked at each of the men, and then asked, 'How fast can you run?'

The men all boasted that they were very swift and took turns to show their speed. Each ran to the end of the beach and back. The old lady shook her head.

'That will not do,' she said, 'none of you is fast enough.' So Oriparoa ran to the first headland and back. Still the old woman shook her head. Only Manini had not run. Now it was his turn.

To everyone's amazement and delight he raced across the distance as though he had wings on his feet, but the old woman was still doubtful.

'Run again,' she commanded.

As Manini raced off again, Oriparoa began to make fire. Manini sped to the fourth headland, and when he returned Oriparoa's fire was still not burning. The old woman was satisfied, and final

40

plans were laid. Every man took his appointed place while Manini prepared to go off and find the dreaded Pouakai. Soon all was ready, and Manini set off to where the old lady had said he would find the giant bird. Over the first row of hills he went, then the second, and then the third, until finally he came to the tenth. At the end of the headland was a cliff. Manini walked to the end of the cliff and looked down.

There was the awe-inspiring bird. Never had Manini seen anything so ugly and so fearsome. It was so big that although it was standing in deep water the tops of its legs could still be seen. And it was gathering fish with its wing, scooping whole schools of them into its mouth.

Manini stifled his fear, took a deep breath, and screamed at the bird.

'Yah! You great ugly beast!'

The great bird swung her head towards Manini. Its bulbous eyes fastened on him, and a bloodcurdling screech rasped its throat. With one mighty thrust of its wings the bird rose into the air.

Manini sped away. Never had he run so fast. Never had his heart beat so loudly. Never had his breath come in such short, agonised gasps. And the screech and flapping of the Pouakai seemed to be just behind him. He must not look! He must not hesitate! He must not fall! Run! Run! Run!

At last the house was before him. The door loomed larger and larger. Only a few more stops, three, two, one, and he was diving through the door just as the wing of the Pouakai thrashed down behind him. The house quaked under the impact, but it stood firm.

Enraged and screaming with anger the bird thrust its wing through the door and swept the floor of the house with it. Down came the centre posts of the house onto the bird's wing, pinning it to the floor. Oriparoa and his men lashed at the wing until only a stump was left. Maddened still further, the bird thrust its other wing into the house, sweeping the limb back and forth while the men clung to the walls and swung their weapons at it. That wing also was soon dismembered. The Pouakai withdrew. From a short distance it looked at the house with fire in its eyes. It circled the house a few times and then swung its beak at the walls. But still the house stood firm. Crazy with hate the bird rushed again at the door and forced its whole head inside. Every weapon struck at the same time, the great Pouakai fell to the ground and died.

When later the bird was torn open they found inside it the bones of thousands of men, and many beautiful greenstone ornaments.

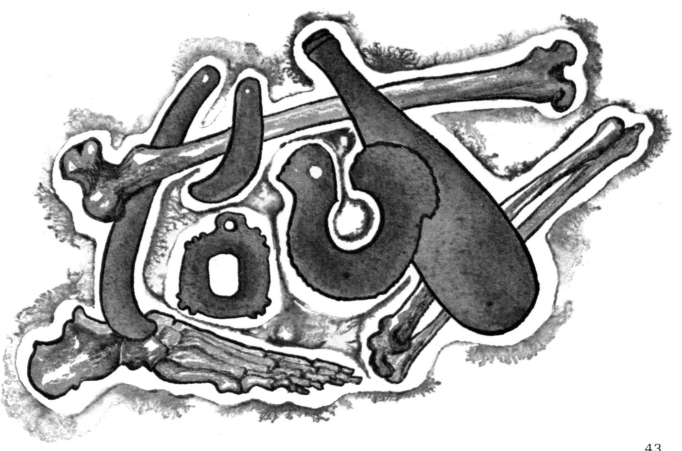

RATA AND THE TOTARA TREE

As the years passed, the enmity between the children of Tu and the children of Tane, Tangaroa, Haumia, and Rongo began to fade. Men learnt that when they showed respect to the gods, the gods were kind. Rongo allowed their crops to flourish, Tangaroa permitted them bountiful supplies of fish to eat, and Tane provided his giant trees with which to build canoes and houses. As long as men performed the proper ceremonies and observed the tapu of the bush, the sea, and planting they were rewarded handsomely, but when sometimes they forgot to perform the ceremonies or deliberately broke the tapu they were punished. When men disregarded the tapu and law of planting, Rongo was offended and caused their crops to wither and drop to the ground. When men cooked the gifts of Tangaroa on the beach and threw the bones and empty shells onto the sea, Tangaroa was insulted and would call all his children away. Not a mussel, or paua, or pipi, or tiny fish would be found again on that beach.

This story, however, is about a man who offended Tane. This man was Rata, an expert canoe builder whose work was both swift and beautiful. He had been commanded by his chief to build a canoe large enough to take his people on a long voyage. He had to have the largest totara tree he could find, and it took him many days tramping through the forest before he found one suitable. When he stumbled upon this giant totara he was so impressed by its magnificent height and breadth that he forgot about the traditional ceremonies and ordered his men to chop it down.

It took many men all day to fell that tree and when at last it came crashing to the ground it was time to go home. Early the next morning Rata and his men returned to the forest, eager to begin work on the new canoe. But when they arrived at the spot where the tree had been felled, behold, there in all its majesty, with its head towering above all the other trees, was the giant totara. There was not an axe-mark or a wood chip anywhere to be seen. It was as though the tree had not been touched, for it was standing erect and whole again.

The forest was ringing with the chirping of insects and the fluting of birds, but when the first axe again bit into the totara tree all the sounds of the bush stopped. Only the chomp, chomp, chomp of axes echoed through the forest.

When the great tree crashed again to the ground Rata ordered his men to chop off its giant crown and its side branches. The great tree looked pathetically naked on the soft earth as Rata and his men gathered their tools together and returned home.

Yet the next day, too, the tree was as whole and as perfect as before. Every branch was in place and each leaf which had been bruised and crushed the previous day was once more smooth and crisp. Rata knew that some strange magic was abroad, and he determined to discover what it was. The tree was felled again, and then Rata and his men began the long trek home. As soon as evening closed in, however, Rata bade his men continue without him, and very quietly he retraced his steps to the spot where the totara tree had been felled.

Night had descended when he arrived, and the moon cast a pale light through the branches of the trees. Rata hid himself in the bushes and waited. The totara log lay where it had been felled, amid wood chips, crushed leaves, and heaps of broken branches. Then suddenly the air was filled with the hum of insects and the flapping of wings. Myriads of birds, butterflies, moths, and beetles blotted out the thick bush as they descended upon the fallen tree. Like a great giant rising from sleep the totara log was lifted back into position and every branch, leaf, and wood chip attached to its former place.

Rata shivered in awe at the spectacle of the tree standing again resplendent in the verdancy of the forest as the last of the birds and insects winged away into the darkness. Only then did he realise that he had not performed the rituals to Tane. He slept among the giant roots of the totara that night, wishing he did not need to fell such a magnificent tree, and next day he rose early. As the first red lights of approaching dawn touched the uppermost tips of the totara he recited a long chant of invocation to the god Tane.

That evening the tree again lay on the bush floor, but Rata did not return home with his men. Instead, he hid himself again to see what would happen. As before, as soon as the moon glimmered through the trees, the winged children of Tane descended. This time they did not return the tree to its former glory. The million tiny beaks pecked at the sides of the totara log until there before the astounded eyes of Rata lay the most beautifully shaped and hollowed canoe he had ever seen.

Rata knew that the spirit of the tree had not flown but was there within the canoe to give it a new life. The giant totara, which had been king of the forest, would now be king of the high seas.

POU AND THE BIRD OF RUA-KAPANGA

Tangaroa, Tane, Haumia, and Rongo became the friends of men. As men thrust their way through the waves of the open sea in search of adventure, Tane and Tangaroa watched over them. Sometimes Tane sent his winged children to serve as guides — the frigate bird, the petrel, and the shining cuckoo. Tangaroa also provided guides — the whale, the porpoise, and sometimes even the giant octopus — while Rongo bestowed upon men his nourishing provisions.

Men were assisted in these ways during their long voyage from Hawaiki to the new land of Aotearoa, a voyage which took place many hundreds of years prior to this story. One man to make the journey did so on the back of a friendly whale, and now one of his descendants by the name of Pou was living at Turangarere in Aotearoa.

Pou was a good husband to his wife, and when their child was born he was also a devoted father. The baby lacked for nothing. His mother's milk was rich with the fat pigeon and the juicy fish which Pou brought home for him to eat. So the child was strong and healthy, and he delighted every moment of his father's life.

One day as Pou returned home with a large catch of whitebait he was met by a very anxious wife.

'Pou,' she said. 'I am worried. The baby has not eaten all day. He refuses to suck from my breast. He must be ill.'

Pou went immediately to see the child. No excited giggles greeted him as he lifted his son in his arms. Instead the child lay limp and flaccid.

'Perhaps he needs different food,' suggested Pou, 'some fish perhaps, or the flesh of the pigeon, or mashed fern root.'

'I think he is yet too small,' said his wife. 'I have tried to feed him those things and even soup from the head of the hapuka, but he refuses them all.'

'Then fetch the tohunga,' said Pou, 'and see what he has to say.'

The tohunga was a man of profound knowledge from whom

Pou had learnt all the ancient law of his people. He was very wise, and he loved children. The child of Pou would one day be chief, so the old tohunga came quickly. He examined the baby very carefully, looking into his mouth and eyes and ears and feeling his body all over. The tohunga looked perplexed.

'It is very strange,' he said. 'The child is perfectly healthy. He suffers no illness. This is beyond my knowledge. I must consult the gods.' Some time later he returned. 'It is very sad,' he said, 'Omens tell me that your child is in need of a very special food, one about which we know nothing. See how the child's tongue protrudes. It points always in the same direction. You must go that way to seek this new food.'

'He is pointing to the vast open sea,' exclaimed Pou.

'Then that is the way you must go,' declared the tohunga.

Pou wasted no time. He went down to the beach and called upon the gods to help him. Tangaroa heard him and sent his swiftest whale, the same whale which had brought Pou's ancestor to this new land many years ago. Perched on the back of the whale, Pou arrived at the island of Rangiatua in a very short time. The people of the island were very kind to him and they treated him royally. When food was placed before him and Pou tasted it, he knew at once that this must be the food which his child craved. It was yellow kumara baked to a golden brown in the earth oven.

Pou was anxious to return home but the proper courtesies had to be observed. Not until after the feasting and the dancing did he speak with the local chief, Rua-Kapanga, who was more than pleased to help when he heard of Pou's need. Not only did he bid his people bring a large basket of the precious food, but he also ordered them to bring a great bird. Pou had never before seen a bird so large. Its legs were as tall as a man.

'This is my pet moa,' explained the chief. 'He will carry you back to your own land very quickly. Take him as your guide and accept the basket of kumara with my blessing.'

'You are indeed a great rangatira,' said Pou. 'For this kindness I wish you a long and prosperous life.'

The giant bird squatted on the ground, and Pou took hold of its huge feathers to pull himself up. Then the basket of kumara was handed to him.

'E noho ra!' called Pou.

'Haere ra!' the people answered together.

The great bird stood erect, and then lifting its giant feet took several strides along the beach before it raised its enormous wings and soared upwards into the sky. The air was icy like the snows of Mount Hikurangi, but Pou nestled among the downy feathers of the bird's back and was quite warm. He could not see anything, for banks of clouds obliterated his view, but he had to keep a sharp lookout for the peak of Hikurangi.

On this mountain lived a ravenous taniwha who captured men and birds with its whiplike tongue. Its tongue was so long that it extended for several miles into the sky. The bird of Rua-Kapanga

was now beginning to descend, and as it came out of the blanket of cloud the sun-drenched peak of Hikurangi came into view. Pou strained his eyes to see whether there were any signs of the taniwha. He saw the snakelike tongue flicking skywards.

'Wait,' Pou ordered the giant bird. 'The taniwha has seen us.'

Just in time, as the flicking tongue swept out towards them, the giant bird rose into another bank of cloud.

'Stay in the cloud,' commanded Pou, 'Let us travel in the cloud.'

The bird obeyed. After what seemed an endless period of time the cloud parted over the mountain. They were flying over the sea again, far out of reach but still within earshot of the thunderous roar of the taniwha which was bellowing his anger at them.

Up the coastline they flew until the bay of Turangarere was in view. As they came in to land Pou could not contain his excitement, and he accidently plucked three feathers from the back of the great bird. The feathers fluttered down onto an island

in the bay and are still there to this day — three kahikatea trees growing on an all but bare little island.

Pou was welcomed home amid great excitement. Both the bird and the new food were a source of wonder to all his people. Some of the precious tubers were placed in the care of the tohunga so that they might be planted at the right time, some were stored away for Pou's son, and the rest were cooked so that all might enjoy them. The kumara became a most valued crop and to this day grows profusely at Turangarere.

The bird of Rua-Kapanga stayed for a long time among the people of Pou. Its many children wandered through the flat grasslands of the coast. One day, however, the bird disappeared. Some say it was killed, others say it died, but many believe that the taniwha of Hikurangi captured it when it was flying home.

THE BOY AND THE SEEDPOD CANOE

Many years ago there was a boy called Tau-tini-awhi-tia. He was a strong, adventurous boy and very clever too. He could sail a canoe all by himself. He could spin a top faster than any of the other boys. His kite always flew higher. And when the boys went into the bush to catch little birds Tau always caught the most. In fact he was so clever that the other boys became jealous and began to tease him.

'Who cares if you are clever?' they teased. 'You have no father like us. Ha, ha, where is your father, fatherless boy?'

And soon all the children began to chant, 'He's got no father! He's got no father! Fatherless, fatherless boy!'

Poor Tau was so ashamed that he ran home and cried and cried. And when he had no more tears he said to his mother, 'Mother, who is my father?'

His mother answered simply, 'Your father is Porou-ano-ano.'

'Where is he?' asked Tau.

'Far, far away,' his mother replied. 'Over there towards the sunrise. That is where your father lives.'

'Will you tell me about him?' asked Tau.

His mother nodded and said, 'Yes, I will tell you.'

She sat beside Tau, was silent for a moment, and then said, 'Your father is a chief from another place. He came here many years ago to visit our village. We fell in love. For many months we were together, and soon you began to grow in my belly.

'They were indeed happy times. I used to hunger for the huia bird and the white heron, and one night your father took his snares and went out to catch the birds. When he brought the birds to me, however, I could not eat them. They were so beautiful. Instead I put them in a cage and kept them for pets.

'But soon your father had to leave. He had to return to his own people. He had to leave even before you were born.'

Tau went into the forest wondering what he should do. 'I cannot stay here any longer,' he thought, 'I must go to my father. I shall have to find a canoe. And I will paddle everywhere until I find him.'

Just then he spied the giant pod of the rewarewa tree. It was shaped like a canoe. It had a prow and a stern post. But would it float? Would it stay upright?

Tau took the pod to the stream and pushed it into the water. The pod floated beautifully and it did not capsize. At once Tau returned to his mother.

'Mother,' he said, 'I am going to find my father. Which way shall I go? Where shall I find him?'

'Towards the sunrise,' replied his mother, 'but the way is long and treacherous. It harbours mighty storms and terrible sea monsters.'

'I must go!' Tau said firmly.

'Then wait until I have cooked some food. You should eat before you go.'

'No, I cannot eat,' said Tau. 'I must go immediately!'

Beside the seedpod canoe Tau and his mother wept together. Perhaps they would never see each other again. Perhaps the frail canoe would not survive the long journey. Yet they both knew Tau had to go. He could never be a man until his father honoured him.

So away went Tau on the seedpod canoe, and his mother watched him from the shore until he had disappeared. Then she began to chant a magic song. Over and over again she chanted until all the monsters of the deep could hear. Even the winds stopped blowing so that they could listen to her beautiful voice. And while they listened she charmed them:

> Be still o monsters of the deep,
> Be still o wind and storm,
> Glide swiftly o canoe
> Make short the distance
> Between this and the far east land
> Until the journey's end.

And so Tau reached his father's land safely.

Soon the children of this village were swarming on the beach.

'A stranger! A stranger!' they shouted, and every child claimed him.

'I saw him first. He will be my slave!' shouted one child.

'No, he is mine! He's mine! He's mine!' they all shouted.

And they all took him to the village arguing, along the way. Finally, after a great deal of fuss and argument, it was agreed that the stranger should become the slave of the smallest child who had been on the beach.

It so happened that this child was also a son of Tau's father, and he ran home to his father dragging Tau after him.

'Look, father!' he exclaimed. 'Look at my slave!'

'Well, well,' said his father, 'what a handsome slave! And what will you do with him?'

'Why he will cook for me, of course!' exclaimed the child.

'Then perhaps you should take him to the cookhouse,' said the father chuckling. And Tau was shown to the cookhouse.

The next day, while the children were playing, Tau went to the forest and trapped a huia bird and a white heron. He kept the birds in the cookhouse, and when nobody was about he began teaching the birds to speak.

He taught the huia bird to say, 'This firelight, it is dim! It is dim! It is dim!'

And he taught the white heron to say, 'This firelight, it is glowing! It is glowing! It is glowing!'

Later that night, when everything was quiet Tau crept over to the sleeping house to investigate. Everyone was asleep, so he fetched his birds and returned. At the front of the sleeping house he stopped and listened. There was no sound but the snoring of the sleeping people. Tau pushed the door open and entered.

Very quietly he tiptoed to the fireplace in the centre of the house and placed the birds in their cage beside the ashes of the fire. At once the huia bird cried out, 'This firelight, it is dim! It is dim! It is dim!'

The people awoke and gasped, they were so amazed. One of the men lifted the cage from the ashes to look at the birds more closely. Immediately the white heron cried out, 'This firelight, it is glowing! It is glowing! It is glowing!'

At this the astonished people rose from their beds to gaze in wonder at these remarkable birds. They shouted applause and clapped their hands in admiration. Tau's father also rose from his bed, and when he looked at the birds he knew at once who Tau was.

'This is my son!' he declared and wept over Tau, and in the morning he performed over him the special ceremony which marked and honoured Tau, the son of a chief.